Bears Make the Best MATHS BUDDIES

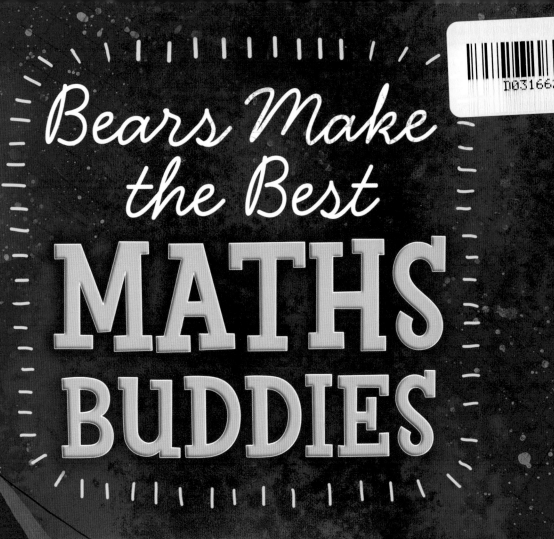

written by
CARMEN OLIVER

illustrated by
JEAN CLAUDE

Raintree is an imprint of Capstone Global Library Limited, a company
incorporated in England and Wales having its registered office at 264
Banbury Road, Oxford, OX2 7DY – Registered company number:
6695582

www.raintree.co.uk
myorders@raintree.co.uk

ISBN 978-1-4747-8722-2

Printed and bound in India

For Erzsi, you are the sum of all things extraordinary.
Thank you for your vision, guidance and faith in me. – C.O.

To João and Luís, all my love – J.C.

"It's time for our maths lesson. Everyone pair up with a buddy," said Mrs Fitz-Pea.

Everyone did – except for Adelaide.

"Oh dear," said Mrs Fitz-Pea. "We have a problem. We're one pupil short."

"Don't worry," said Adelaide. "I have the answer."

1 + 2

2 + 4

3 +

4 + 3

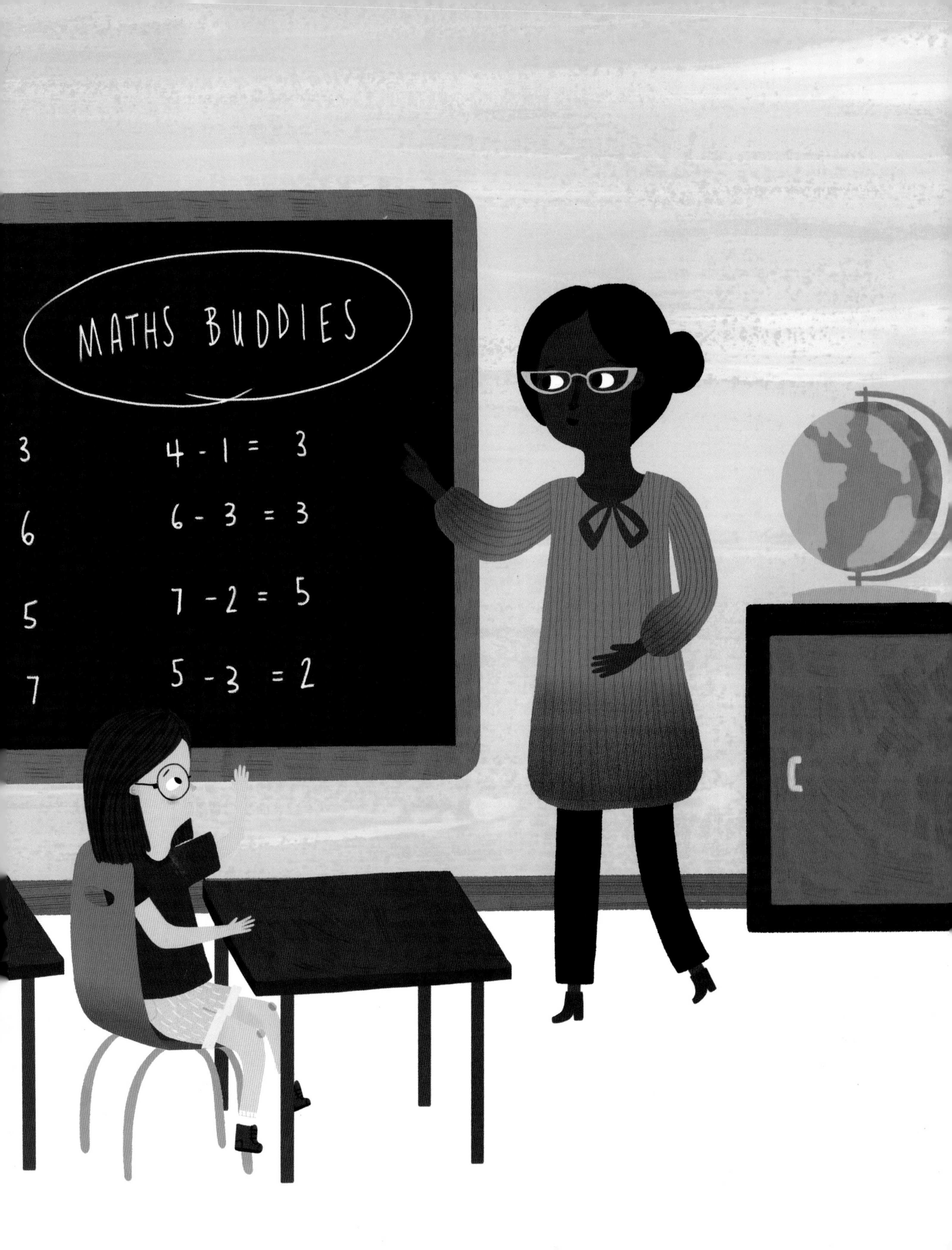
MATHS BUDDIES
3
4 - 1 = 3
6
6 - 3 = 3
5
7 - 2 = 5
7
5 - 3 = 2

"You can do this," Adelaide whispered. "Come on."

Bear grunted and followed Adelaide.

$$1 + 2 = 3$$
$$2 + 4 = 6$$
$$3 + 2 = 5$$
$$4 + 3 = 7$$

"I know Bear was a good reading buddy," said Mrs Fitz-Pea. "But reading is one thing. Maths? I'm not sure."

S BUDDIES

$4 - 1 = 3$

$6 - 3 = 3$

$7 - 2 = 5$

$5 - 3 = 2$

"Bears make the best maths buddies," said Adelaide.
"It's simply a fact. They know how to put one paw
in front of the other and measure any distance."

"Of course, they never get directions mixed up. They know north is at 12 o'clock, east is at 3 o'clock, south is at 6 o'clock, and west is at 9 o'clock."

"Bears make the best maths buddies because they have great imaginations. As the clouds drift by, they see different shapes everywhere they look. Circles, triangles, squares and rectangles."

"In the river, catching fish takes practice. Bears never ever give up. Before long, the salmon add up."

$$1 + 1 + 1 + 2 = 5$$

"Bear is clever. He can say 'subtract'."

$$5 - 2 = 3$$

"Bears make the best maths buddies because every night they count the stars until they fall asleep."

1, 2, 3, 4, 5, 6, 7, 8, 9, 10 . . .

7

10

9

8

"In the morning, they're very hungry and collect lots of berries. But before they gobble them up . . .

. . . they sort them into groups. They work out how many groups there are and how many berries they have in each group."

"Bears make the best maths buddies because they know that some maths you can get wrong. Sometimes you make a few mistakes, turn over a few rocks and really dig deep to discover the solution."

"And when you get it right . . .

. . . they spring into action and

ROARRR!

They knew you could do it all along."

"They know that whether you're in the classroom or out in the big wide world . . .

... maths is everywhere. There's a pattern in everything. Solving puzzles is fun!"

"Is there anything this bear can't do?"
Mrs Fitz-Pea asked.

$$1 + 2 = 3$$

$$1 + 3 = 4$$

$$1 + 4 = 5$$

$$2 + 2 = 4$$

2

"No," said Adelaide. "He understands everything."

"Well, that sums up that problem," said Mrs Fitz-Pea.

$$2 \times 2 = 4$$

$$2 \times 3 = 6$$

$$2 \times 4 = 8$$

$$2 \times 5 = 10$$

$$2 \times 6 = 12$$

"Do you think we should tell her that you're great at writing too?" Adelaide asked.

Bear just grinned.